Adapted by Beth Goodman
Based on the motion picture written by Jim Strain

SCHOLASTIC INC.
New York Toronto London Auckland Sydney

TRI-STAR PICTURES PRESENTS "BINGO" CINDY WILLIAMS DAVID RASCHE
MUSIC BY JOHN MORRIS
WRITTEN BY JIM STRAIN PRODUCED BY THOMAS BAER DIRECTED BY MATTHEW ROBBINS
A TRI-STAR RELEASE
© 1991 TRI-STAR PICTURES, INC. ALL RIGHTS RESERVED

ISBN 0-590-45039-5

12 11 10 9 8 7 6 5 4 3   1 2 3 4 5 6/9

Printed in the U.S.A.   24

First Scholastic printing, August 1991

Bingo lives at the Hannibal-Hamlin Family Circus. He is a very unusual dog. He likes to visit the clowns. That's just where he is now. Suddenly he remembers that he has a job to do. He grabs a bucket, fills it with water, and brings it to his owners, Steve and Ginger. Whoops! The water spills.

"Look what you've done! You're hopeless!" Steve yells.
Poor Bingo.

Just then, Lauren the poodle walks by. Steve and Ginger
notice she's limping. Lauren has stepped on a nail. She will
never be well enough to go on with tonight's show.

"Why not use Bingo?" suggests Ginger.

"Bingo?" Steve asks in a puzzled voice.

Then Steve realizes that Bingo is the only choice.

It's show time! Bingo walks onto the platform. He has to jump through a fiery hoop. But Bingo won't jump through it. He just sits and stares at it.

"Jump! Jump!" yells Steve.

But Bingo is afraid. He thinks back to when he was a puppy. Back then, he was living in a pet store with his mother. One day, there was a huge fire in the store. Little Bingo lost his mother.

Steve is now furious with Bingo for ruining his act. He heads for Bingo but Ginger stops him.

"Run, Bingo! Escape! Start a new life," Ginger pleads.

Bingo sadly leaves the circus. He will miss his friends.

After walking for a while, Bingo looks back at his old home. The tents are now tiny specks in the distance. Bingo decides to set up camp for the night.

The next morning, he sees a boy lying in a stream! The boy is hurt. He has fallen off his bicycle.

It's Bingo to the rescue! Bingo pulls the boy out of the stream. Uh-oh! The boy isn't breathing! Bingo thinks quickly. He jumps onto the boy's chest and the boy spits out all the water he swallowed.

"I'm Chuckie," says the boy. "You saved my life. You and I are gonna be friends for life. Right?"

Bingo barks. He's happy he has made a friend.

"There was a kid who had a dog and Bingo was his name-o . . . ," Chuckie sings.

Chuckie says he's starving. Bingo has an idea. He catches a
trout from the stream. But Chuckie isn't the only one who's
hungry. A big, black bear smells the fish!

All of a sudden the bear appears and lets out a huge growl.
Bingo climbs up a tree. Chuckie climbs up after him. Whew!
That was close!

Back at Chuckie's house, his family is having dinner.

"More chuckie? I mean chicken, Chuck. I mean chicken, Chickie!" says Chuckie's mother to his stepbrother, Chickie. "I'm worried about Chuckie," she says to Chuckie's father.

Chickie interrupts. "He's probably just messin' around in the woods."

"If we don't hear anything soon I'll call the police," assures Chuckie's dad.

Chuckie's parents are worried about him. His mother starts to call the police. Just then, she spots Chuckie walking down the street. He and Bingo finally made it safely out of the woods.

Since dogs are not welcome in Chuckie's home, they walk in through the back door. Sneaky Bingo hides in the kitchen cupboard.

The next morning Chuckie eats a big breakfast. Then he goes to get ready for school. When no one is looking, Bingo follows him upstairs. Bingo stays home while Chuckie's mother drives him to school.

Chuckie tries to convince his mother to let him keep Bingo. "You know, Mom, some people think animals are lucky."

"Forget it. No pets!" she says.

School is out and Chuckie rushes home to be with his pal, Bingo. Bingo is happy to see Chuckie. He barks and jumps and is ready to play.

They spend the afternoon having lots of fun! They go to the arcade, they skateboard. Bingo even helps Chuckie with his math homework. What a smart dog!

When Chuckie gets back home his family greets him at the door. They don't look too happy.

"Something got into my cold cream," says his mother.

"Something chewed up my citizenship award," says his brother.

"What are you saying? That I'm hiding a . . . a dog," says Chuckie nervously.

His parents just tell him to pack his bags. The whole family is moving to Wisconsin in the morning. His father is a football player and has been traded to another team.

That night, while Chuckie is sound asleep, Bingo sneaks out of Chuckie's room. He wants to visit the dog that lives next door. In the morning Chuckie looks all over for Bingo. He can't find him anywhere.

"Bingooo!" he calls. There is no answer.

Sad Chuckie gets into the car with the rest of his family. As he looks out the window, tears roll down his face.

As the car is driving down the street, Chuckie suddenly spots Bingo. So do Chuckie's parents.

"So there *was* a dog!" says his mother.

Bingo tries to catch up with the car, but he can't run fast enough. In a busy intersection Bingo loses sight of the car. Then he gets excited. He picks up on Chuckie's scent. Bingo again runs off after his new friend.

After hours of walking in the hot sun, Bingo falls to the ground. He is awakened by a man who carries him into his truck and brings him to Duke's hot dog stand. Bingo is put into a crate with other dogs. Soon Bingo realizes that Duke is a nasty man who wants to hurt him and the other dogs. Bingo knows he has to escape.

Bingo digs an escape tunnel in the ground.

Bingo crawls out of the tunnel and frees himself. He then frees all the other dogs. Duke and his waitresses can't believe what is happening. They're frightened by the dogs.

All the dogs leave the hot dog stand behind them and travel down the road to freedom. When they come to a highway, Bingo leaves the others. He gets a lump in his throat as he waves good-bye to them. Bingo continues his search for his best friend, Chuckie.

Tired and hungry, Bingo looks through a trash can for some food. Just then he hears voices and sees two men. They take him into a trailer.

"Come on, we'll get you some chow," says the man named Lennie.

"Don't touch the cheese!" says the other man, Eli.

Inside the trailer, Bingo knows something fishy is going on. Eli and Lennie are criminals. They are holding a family of four captive!

Bingo waits until Eli and Lennie are sleeping. Then he sneaks out of the trailer to call for help. He dials 9-1-1 and the operator answers. Bingo barks.

"All I can hear is your dog," says the operator. "But we've locked in your number and location."

Bingo goes back to the trailer and unties the family. Just as Lennie and Eli wake up, the police come to the trailer and arrest them.

Bingo is a hero! The Thompson family is grateful to him for saving their lives. Cindy and Sandy Thompson each hug Bingo tight. They take him home to live with them.

Back in a motel, Chuckie sees a TV news story about Bingo's brave deed. He sends Bingo a letter to let the dog know where his family is.

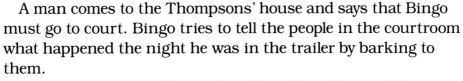

A man comes to the Thompsons' house and says that Bingo must go to court. Bingo tries to tell the people in the courtroom what happened the night he was in the trailer by barking to them.

Bingo's barking confuses the judge. The judge sends him to jail!

In his cell, Bingo uses his great digging skills and starts another escape tunnel! He has to find Chuckie.

A guard brings Bingo a letter that the Thompsons had dropped off. It's the letter from Chuckie! Bingo is so happy! His cell mate reads him the letter.

"I want you to find me so as we can resume our happy life together. Pick up my trail, which I know you were following."

Bingo's cell mate is about to read Chuckie's address. Suddenly, the letter is yanked from his hand.

It's Lennie and Eli! They are in jail, too. They won't give the letter back. Bingo's cell mate wants to protect him from Lennie and Eli. He tries to get the letter back. The letters rips!

Later that night, Bingo's cell mate rolls out of bed and wakes Bingo.

"It's time," his cell mate says.

They crawl through the escape tunnel and make it out of jail without getting caught.

Bingo and his cell mate say good-bye to each other, and Bingo continues his search for Chuckie.

Bingo finally traces the letter back to the motel it was mailed from. He has traveled a great distance. At the motel, a woman named Bunny finds Bingo exhausted. He's been following Chuckie's scent for so long that his nose is completely worn out!

Bunny takes sick Bingo to the vet. Bingo needs an operation so that his nose will work again.

"He's overworked his own nose," says the vet.

The operation goes well, and Bingo's nose works just as well as ever!

But Bingo is sad. He thought he'd find Chuckie at the motel. Bunny helps Bingo. She finds out Chuckie's new address from a man working in the motel. She takes Bingo to the bus station and wishes him luck.

The bus pulls into another station. It's Green Bay, where Chuckie now lives. Bingo finds Chuckie's new street. He sees Chuckie walking down the street. But wait. He is walking another dog! It's only a neighbor's dog, but Bingo doesn't know that. Bingo is heartbroken. He whimpers and sadly walks away.

Bingo wanders into a garbage dump behind Vic's restaurant. He looks for scraps of food. Vic sees Bingo and gives him a job. Bingo is a great dishwasher!

Meanwhile, Lennie and Eli have escaped from jail and are following Bingo. They hang posters all over Green Bay. The posters say there's a $500 reward for a lost dog and they include a drawing of Bingo.

Chuckie sees one of the posters. That's Bingo! He races off on his bicycle to the address on the poster. But a man beats him to the address. The man works with Bingo at Vic's. He tells Lennie and Eli where Bingo can be found. They go off to get the dog, and Chuckie follows them.

Eli and Lennie get to Vic's, and just as they grab Bingo,
Chuckie rides his bicycle right into Lennie!
"Let go of my dog!" Chuckie demands. "Run, Bingo! Run!"
They grab Chuckie instead and drive off with him!
No one knows it, but Bingo is riding along on top of the car!

They stop the car at an old warehouse. The two men bring Chuckie inside and hold him prisoner. They set up a bomb and hide it in a suitcase! Bingo watches the whole thing. He runs to Chuckie's house for help.

Chickie opens the door and sees Bingo with Chuckie's hat in his mouth. But Chickie doesn't know that the hat belongs to his brother. He closes the door in Bingo's face.

Then the telephone rings. Chuckie's mother answers it.

"We've got your kid!" says the voice on the other end.

"Someone's got Chuckie!" calls his mother. "That dog may know where he is."

Chickie follows Bingo to the warehouse, and his mother calls his father at the football game.

"Kidnappers have got Chuckie! If we want to see him again they want you to miss all your field goals," she tells Chuckie's dad.

Eli and Lennie want Chuckie's father to lose the game for his team so they can win a lot of money!

Chickie goes home to tell his mother where Chuckie is. Bingo goes into the warehouse to try to help his friend. But Eli and Lennie catch him and tie him and Chuckie up. They leave the warehouse.

Chickie, his mother, and the sheriff go to the warehouse. Meanwhile, Bingo chews through his rope. A fire starts in the warehouse! He tries to untie Chuckie, but he can't!

"It's no use. Try to set off the fire alarm," cries Chuckie.

Bingo is brave. He leaps through the fire, over to the alarm, and sets it off!

Chickie, his mother, and the sheriff get to the warehouse. So do the fire fighters. The sheriff sees Lennie and Eli hiding in a car. He arrests them.

The fire fighters go into the warehouse to rescue Chuckie. Bingo wants to help. He sees the suitcase with the bomb and carries it out of the warehouse. Just as he gets outside the bomb accidentally goes off!

The fire fighters run out of the warehouse with Chuckie. They see Bingo. He has been hurt. They bring the boy and the dog to the hospital.

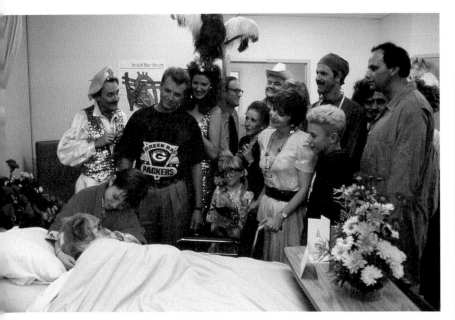

At the hospital, Chuckie's family is gathered around his bed. Chuckie's mom had called his dad at the game, when Chuckie was safe. His father was so happy that he kicked a field goal and won the game for his team.

"How is Bingo?" asks Chuckie.

Chuckie gets wheeled into Bingo's room to see for himself. There are so many people in the room. Everyone Bingo met on his travels is there! They all heard Bingo's story on the news and came to wish him well.

Chuckie pets Bingo. Bingo's eyes open wide. He barks. Chuckie gives him a big hug.

Bingo and Chuckie are together, forever, at last!